Through the Eyes of Priya

A TRUE STORY

By Carole Davey

Illustrated by Deborah Henning

Tadorna Press
Ithaca, New York

Published by Tadorna Press, Ithaca, New York
ISBN Number: 978-0-9915781-7-7
Printed in the United States of America
First Edition 2018
Second Printing 2019

Production Management: Della R. Mancuso
Editing: Our dear friend with an eagle eye, Margaret A. Custer
Cover Design and Graphics: A wonderfully talented friend

We would like to thank two very big hearts,
Carol and Mack Travis, for seeing the light of consciousness shining
so brightly within all beings and for making this book possible.

Dedicated to the cows,
the great nourishers of life,
and to the children
who are going to help create a
happy, healthy, and
compassionate world.

Hi. I'm a Jersey cow, and I was born on a small dairy farm. I would tell you my name, but I don't have one yet. When I was very young, some humans stapled something to my ear. I used to go cross-eyed trying to see what it was. Finally, one of my little calf friends told me that it was my number card. That's what I was— a number.

Jersey cows range from being a light blond like me to a dark brunette like a lot of my friends. We are not those black and white cows that you see everywhere. They are Holsteins. Holsteins are more docile than Jerseys. Holsteins are always very well-mannered and obedient. They never buck the system, whereas Jersey cows can be extremely stubborn. Once we dig our hooves in, no matter how much you pull and prod us, we won't move. The upside is that we are very loving (if we're in a good mood) and very loyal to our family and friends. We are also creative and can think of many ways to knock down a fence if the grass is greener on the other side.

5

When I was about two years old, all of us cows overheard our owner say that he was going to sell us and retire. He made arrangements for all of his cows to be taken to the cow market. He was hoping that the pregnant heifer wouldn't give birth until after she was sold, because she was going to bring in the most money. This completely freaked me out! Firstly, these were the only cows I had ever known. Like most dairy cows, I was taken away from my mother a few hours after I was born. The other little calves had become my family. I remember missing my Mom so much! I didn't like the food the farmer gave me either—I wanted my mother's milk.

Secondly… I was the pregnant heifer! A heifer is a cow that hasn't had a calf yet. Once a heifer has her first calf, then she is called a cow. The next morning all my friends were herded into a big truck and driven away. At the last minute, the farmer decided not to send me because he could tell that I was about to give birth.

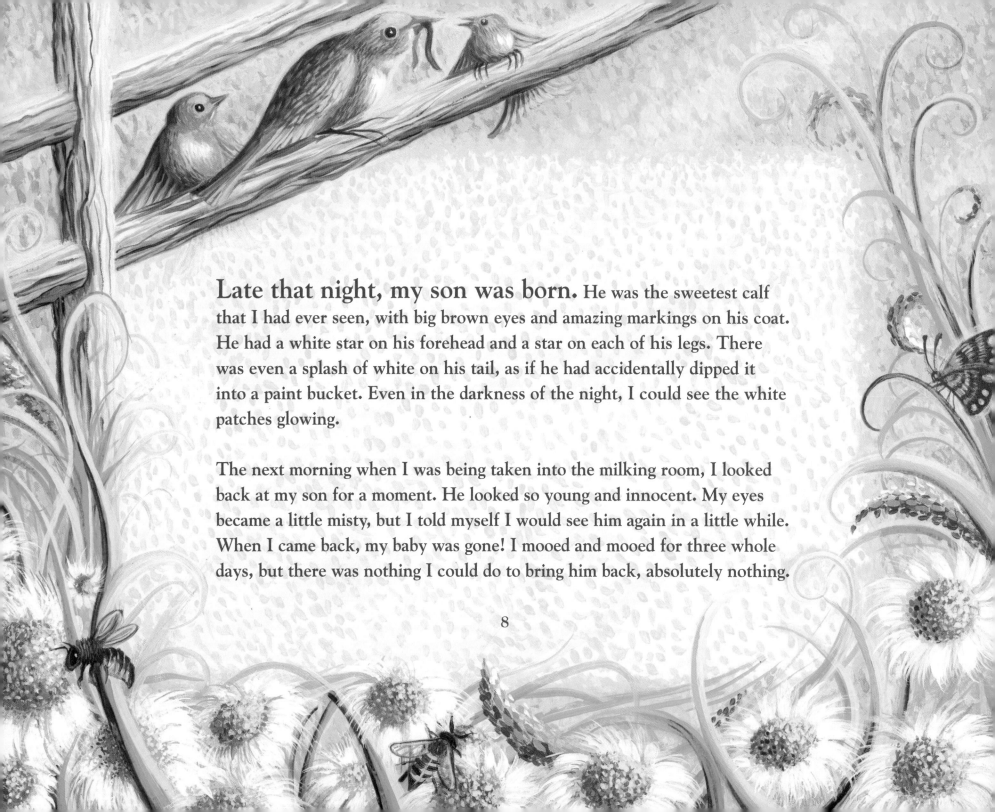

Late that night, my son was born. He was the sweetest calf that I had ever seen, with big brown eyes and amazing markings on his coat. He had a white star on his forehead and a star on each of his legs. There was even a splash of white on his tail, as if he had accidentally dipped it into a paint bucket. Even in the darkness of the night, I could see the white patches glowing.

The next morning when I was being taken into the milking room, I looked back at my son for a moment. He looked so young and innocent. My eyes became a little misty, but I told myself I would see him again in a little while. When I came back, my baby was gone! I mooed and mooed for three whole days, but there was nothing I could do to bring him back, absolutely nothing.

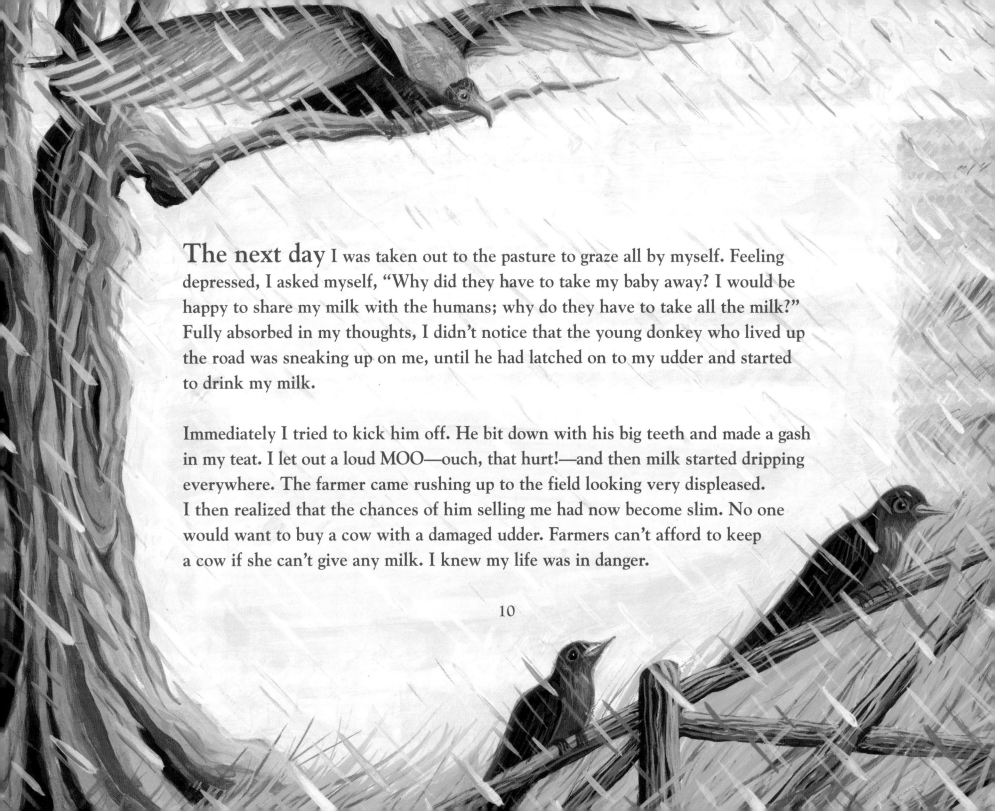

The next day I was taken out to the pasture to graze all by myself. Feeling depressed, I asked myself, "Why did they have to take my baby away? I would be happy to share my milk with the humans; why do they have to take all the milk?" Fully absorbed in my thoughts, I didn't notice that the young donkey who lived up the road was sneaking up on me, until he had latched on to my udder and started to drink my milk.

Immediately I tried to kick him off. He bit down with his big teeth and made a gash in my teat. I let out a loud MOO—ouch, that hurt!—and then milk started dripping everywhere. The farmer came rushing up to the field looking very displeased. I then realized that the chances of him selling me had now become slim. No one would want to buy a cow with a damaged udder. Farmers can't afford to keep a cow if she can't give any milk. I knew my life was in danger.

10

A few days later, a visitor came to the farm. At first, I didn't take much notice. Who cares about visitors when you know that soon you'll be on someone's dinner plate, or worse still, sitting on a shelf in a can of dog food? Not knowing what else to do, I wished for a miracle to save my life.

After a while, I put my head up and saw a human walking toward me. She came right up to me and started stroking my nose and tickling my ears. There was something special about her, and I couldn't quite put my hoof on what it was. We connected on a very deep level—I felt as if I had known her all my life. After a few minutes, she told me that she had come to take me to my new home.

12

My new owner's name was Katherine, and the first thing she did was give me a name. She called me Priya, which means "very precious" or "pretty one." I thought it suited me well.

After I arrived at Katherine's home, I saw my new herd for the first time. These cows sure looked different from my old friends back at the other farm. No one seemed to be scared, grieving, or depressed. They were the happiest cows I had ever seen. It made me wonder what sort of barn I had landed myself in. I kicked myself a couple of times just to make sure I wasn't dreaming.

At first, I was kept in my own pen (not that the others had pens; as far as I could see they could do as they liked). It was a good idea, though, because it helped me settle down and get some sleep. It had been an exciting day.

14

The next morning I noticed two cats staring at me from a fence. Purring loudly, they slowly came over and checked me out. They told me their names were Princess and Bala and this was their barn because they were born here, but they didn't mind sharing it with me and I could stay. I was happy to hear that. It's always good to stay friends with the barn cats because once they love you, they love you forever.

At last I was let out of my pen, and immediately I made a beeline to the food, as I always do, not caring whom I bumped into or pushed aside. To my surprise, they all let me do this. I started feeling quite empowered by this group of cows, and after several months I rose up in the ranks and became their leader. Cows choose their leader by intelligence. I guess I am pretty smart. Plus, I have to admit, I am a bit bossy—even my little calf friends told me I was bossy.

17

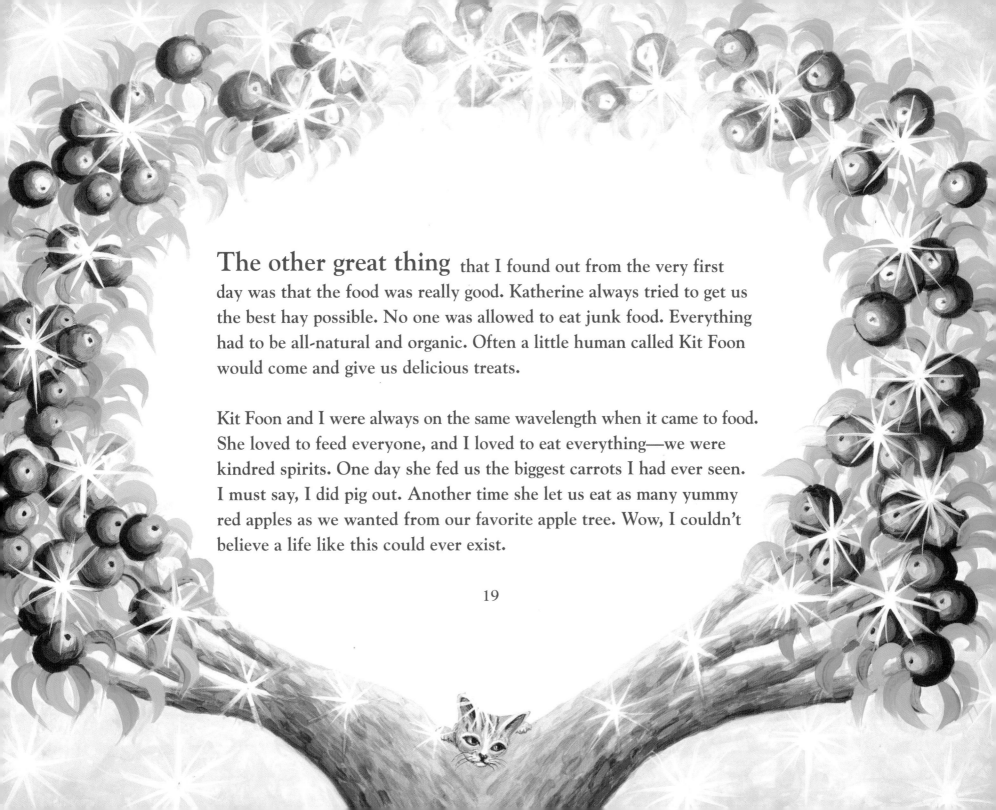

The other great thing that I found out from the very first day was that the food was really good. Katherine always tried to get us the best hay possible. No one was allowed to eat junk food. Everything had to be all-natural and organic. Often a little human called Kit Foon would come and give us delicious treats.

Kit Foon and I were always on the same wavelength when it came to food. She loved to feed everyone, and I loved to eat everything—we were kindred spirits. One day she fed us the biggest carrots I had ever seen. I must say, I did pig out. Another time she let us eat as many yummy red apples as we wanted from our favorite apple tree. Wow, I couldn't believe a life like this could ever exist.

19

The days and weeks went by, and as long as I was first in the food line, life just couldn't be better. I grew to love my herd members very much. Each one of them was special and dear to me. I even became fond of my milkman, Rudi. I never liked the milkmen back at the other place; they were too rough and didn't know how to treat girls like me.

Rudi was different; he had a big heart and a great sense of humor. He treated us like friends. I also liked Rudi's Harley-Davidson hat. One morning I tried to take a bite out of it, but it didn't taste very good, so I spat it back out. He didn't seem to notice. I like the straw hats much better.

20

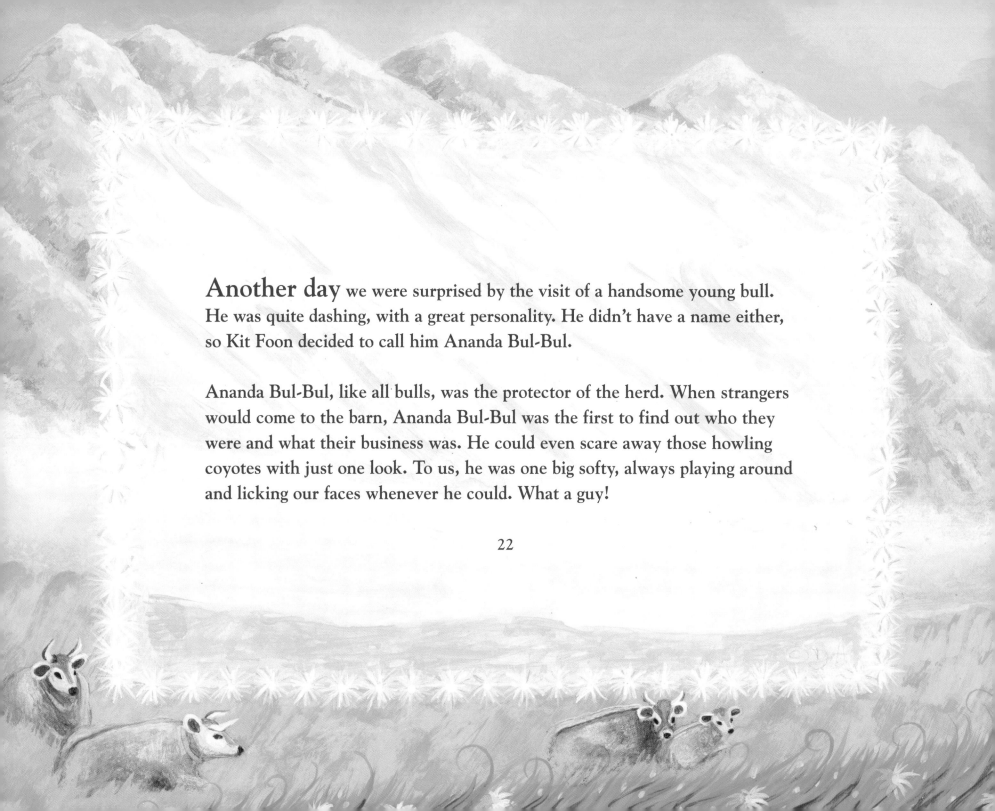

Another day we were surprised by the visit of a handsome young bull. He was quite dashing, with a great personality. He didn't have a name either, so Kit Foon decided to call him Ananda Bul-Bul.

Ananda Bul-Bul, like all bulls, was the protector of the herd. When strangers would come to the barn, Ananda Bul-Bul was the first to find out who they were and what their business was. He could even scare away those howling coyotes with just one look. To us, he was one big softy, always playing around and licking our faces whenever he could. What a guy!

22

Some months passed, and I hadn't been feeling that well for a few days. All of my four tummies felt like they were going through the washing machine. No one knew what was wrong. One of the guys that helped Katherine take care of us named Wayne thought I had been eating too much, but Rudi said, "She always eats too much."

Later that day, they decided to call the vet, whom I didn't care for at all, and I tried my best to kick him away when he was examining me. After all this drama, the vet announced that I would be having a new calf. "A new calf!" I mooed loudly. I then gave that nice vet a big lick right across his face. Wayne, who knew I loved a good neck rub, came over and congratulated me by giving me the most wonderful neck rub ever. It was pure bliss.

The weather had been good, so we had all slept out in the pasture. I loved those summer nights. I felt so relaxed, I couldn't think of anywhere else on earth where I would rather be. This was my home. Then one morning I woke up with a feeling of dread. I couldn't work out what was wrong. My unborn calf was fine; she was a good kicker and had woken me up about ten times during the night.

I decided to wander down to the barn and see if anything new was happening. As I got closer to the barn, I heard the loud voice of a man talking to Katherine. I knew that voice. It was the voice of my previous owner, and then it suddenly flashed across my mind that he was here to take me back. I was panic-stricken. "I'm not going," I said to myself. "I'll run away. He can't take me! I belong here! If I go back he'll take my calf and all my milk and then send me off to the marketplace to be sold."

27

I was pulled out of my thoughts by the sound of my two owners talking.
I had my ears as close as possible to the milk room window. I heard my previous
owner say, "She's my cow. I was only lending her to you. Now I don't have any cows,
and I want the milk." My heart sank. "That's not true, you two-legged fibber—
you didn't want me; nobody wanted me."

Katherine pleaded, "You said that I could have her because you were retiring and
that she couldn't be sold because of her leaking teat." My previous owner started to
become angry and demanded that she give me back. Katherine replied, "How much do
you want for her?" He said flatly, "Fifteen hundred dollars." My heart went tumbling
down. I knew she couldn't afford to pay that much. She was struggling to pay for
everyone's hay. I also knew she didn't need me; she had many other cows. I thought
I should go in and give myself up. I didn't want my herd to go without food
because of me.

28

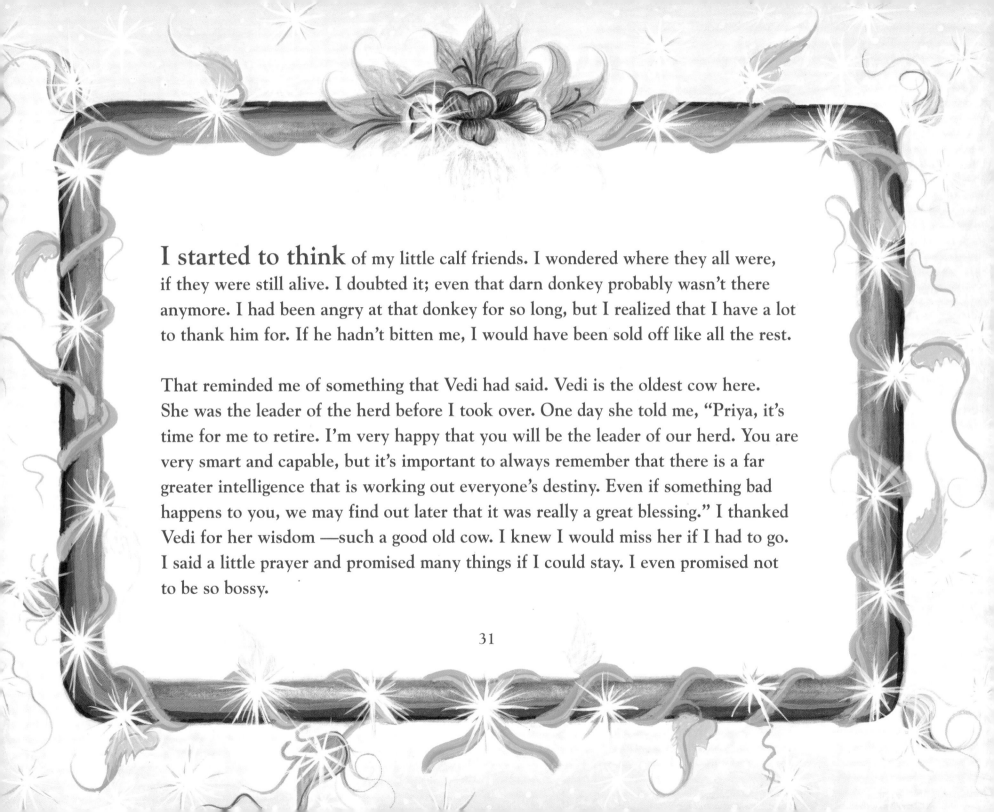

I started to think of my little calf friends. I wondered where they all were, if they were still alive. I doubted it; even that darn donkey probably wasn't there anymore. I had been angry at that donkey for so long, but I realized that I have a lot to thank him for. If he hadn't bitten me, I would have been sold off like all the rest.

That reminded me of something that Vedi had said. Vedi is the oldest cow here. She was the leader of the herd before I took over. One day she told me, "Priya, it's time for me to retire. I'm very happy that you will be the leader of our herd. You are very smart and capable, but it's important to always remember that there is a far greater intelligence that is working out everyone's destiny. Even if something bad happens to you, we may find out later that it was really a great blessing." I thanked Vedi for her wisdom —such a good old cow. I knew I would miss her if I had to go. I said a little prayer and promised many things if I could stay. I even promised not to be so bossy.

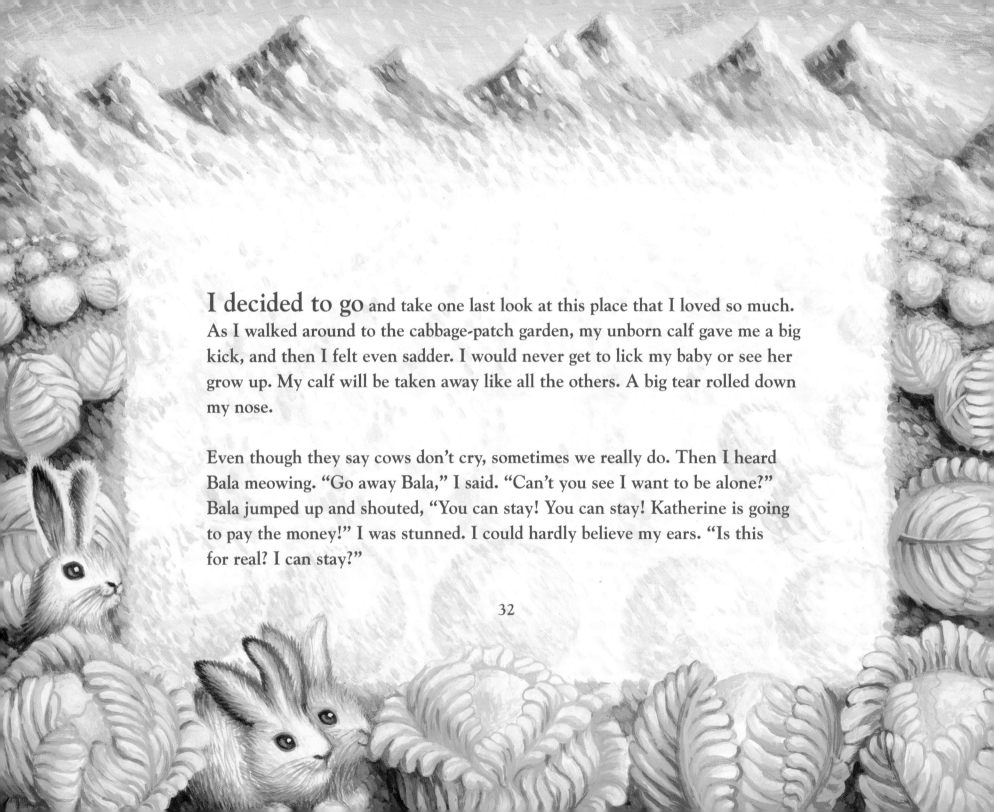

I decided to go and take one last look at this place that I loved so much. As I walked around to the cabbage-patch garden, my unborn calf gave me a big kick, and then I felt even sadder. I would never get to lick my baby or see her grow up. My calf will be taken away like all the others. A big tear rolled down my nose.

Even though they say cows don't cry, sometimes we really do. Then I heard Bala meowing. "Go away Bala," I said. "Can't you see I want to be alone?" Bala jumped up and shouted, "You can stay! You can stay! Katherine is going to pay the money!" I was stunned. I could hardly believe my ears. "Is this for real? I can stay?"

32

I trotted back as fast as I could, and I was just in time to see Katherine coming out of the barn. With a big smile on her face, she laughingly said, "Now, Priya, how are we going to pay for this? Don't worry, we will."

My heart swelled up with love for her. She didn't need me. She did this because she cares that I have a good home and that my calf will be safe and with me, and she cares that I'm allowed to live. With a full heart, I went and placed my head on her feet.

34

The next few months went by really fast. I knew my baby was going to arrive any day—my udder was so big I could hardly walk. I somehow managed to waddle down to some trees by the lake, and very soon my little girl was born. Hooray! It was how I wanted it to be, out in nature with no one around, just the two of us. I spent the first hour licking her. My tongue felt as if it were going to fall off. Soon she was able to stand up and walk around. She was worth every lick.

I looked up at the sky and saw a beautiful rainbow, and then I spotted Wayne coming in the distance. I was so happy to see him and to show off my new calf. Wayne said he found us by following the rainbow. Wayne carried my newborn calf all the way back to the barn with me trotting very close behind.

Back at the barn, many more humans came. I always remember faces, but I'm not so good with names. After a while, I noticed that my baby hadn't starting drinking my milk yet, which was vital for her survival, so I gestured with my head to a couple of the humans to come and help, and to my surprise they understood. They came right into the pen and helped her find my udder. (I didn't see how she could have missed it, since it was so big!) We all felt a huge relief when we heard those first few slurps.

Some special humans were asked to name her, and they decided on Hasita, which they said means happy and free. I approved—it couldn't suit her more. Hasita is like her mother and loves to eat. Every drop of my milk was a drop of love, a drop of pure nectar. Our hearts became one.

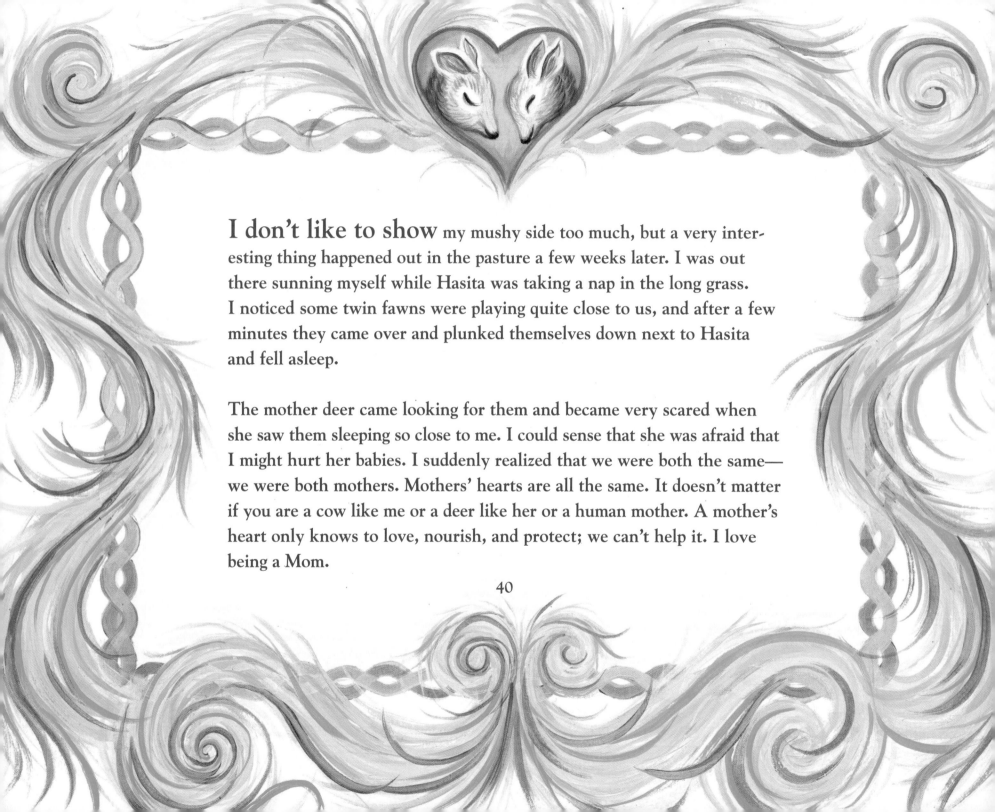

I don't like to show my mushy side too much, but a very interesting thing happened out in the pasture a few weeks later. I was out there sunning myself while Hasita was taking a nap in the long grass. I noticed some twin fawns were playing quite close to us, and after a few minutes they came over and plunked themselves down next to Hasita and fell asleep.

The mother deer came looking for them and became very scared when she saw them sleeping so close to me. I could sense that she was afraid that I might hurt her babies. I suddenly realized that we were both the same— we were both mothers. Mothers' hearts are all the same. It doesn't matter if you are a cow like me or a deer like her or a human mother. A mother's heart only knows to love, nourish, and protect; we can't help it. I love being a Mom.

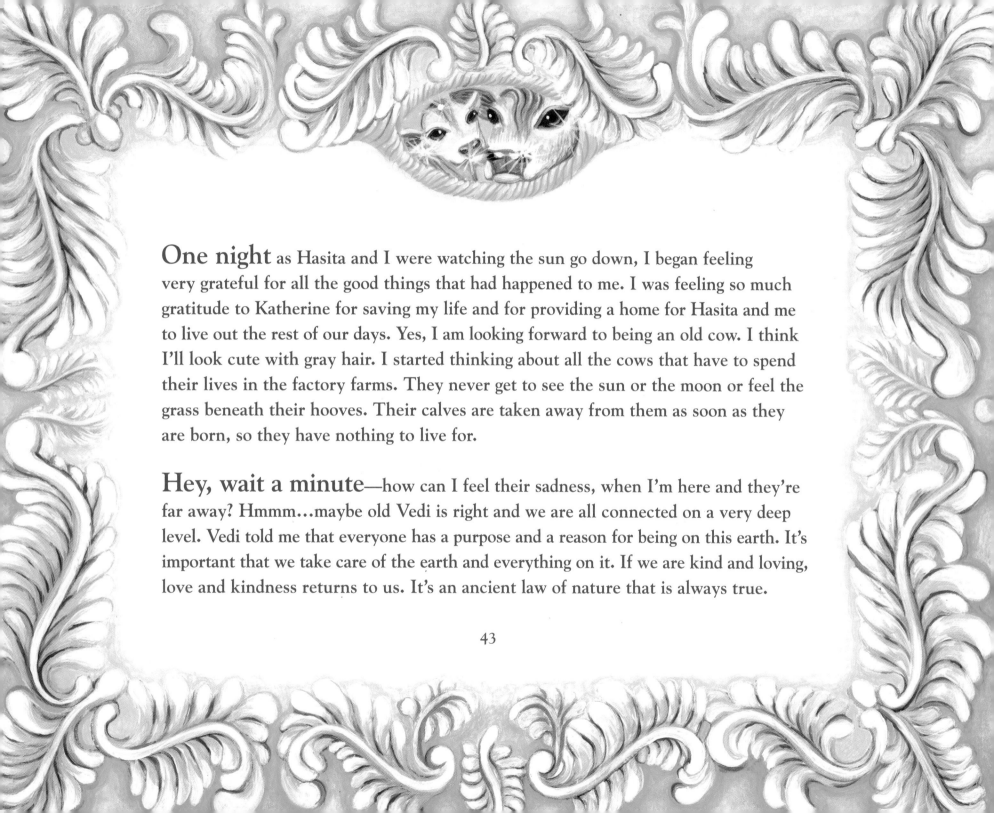

One night as Hasita and I were watching the sun go down, I began feeling very grateful for all the good things that had happened to me. I was feeling so much gratitude to Katherine for saving my life and for providing a home for Hasita and me to live out the rest of our days. Yes, I am looking forward to being an old cow. I think I'll look cute with gray hair. I started thinking about all the cows that have to spend their lives in the factory farms. They never get to see the sun or the moon or feel the grass beneath their hooves. Their calves are taken away from them as soon as they are born, so they have nothing to live for.

Hey, wait a minute—how can I feel their sadness, when I'm here and they're far away? Hmmm…maybe old Vedi is right and we are all connected on a very deep level. Vedi told me that everyone has a purpose and a reason for being on this earth. It's important that we take care of the earth and everything on it. If we are kind and loving, love and kindness returns to us. It's an ancient law of nature that is always true.

Wise old Vedi always inspires me to want to be a good cow. I made a big wish that one day I could do something really great to make this world a better place for all cows. Maybe all I need to do is tell my story and then everyone will understand.

Imagine my human and cow friends all sitting around a campfire together, chomping on fresh green grass and eating carrots under the light of the full moon. It's such a delicious thought…but now I'm getting hungry again.

I bent down and gave Hasita a goodnight lick and then looked up at the stars and said goodnight to my son, wherever he may be. As I was drifting off to sleep, the strangest thing happened—a song came flooding into my mind. "Believe in yourself and miracles can happen. Believe in yourself and believe in the miracle of life."

Katherine

Rudi and Priya

Hasita Learning to Drink

Wise Old Vedi

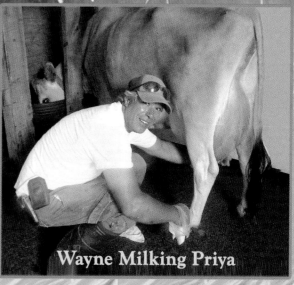
Wayne Milking Priya

Princess

Kit Foon

Bala

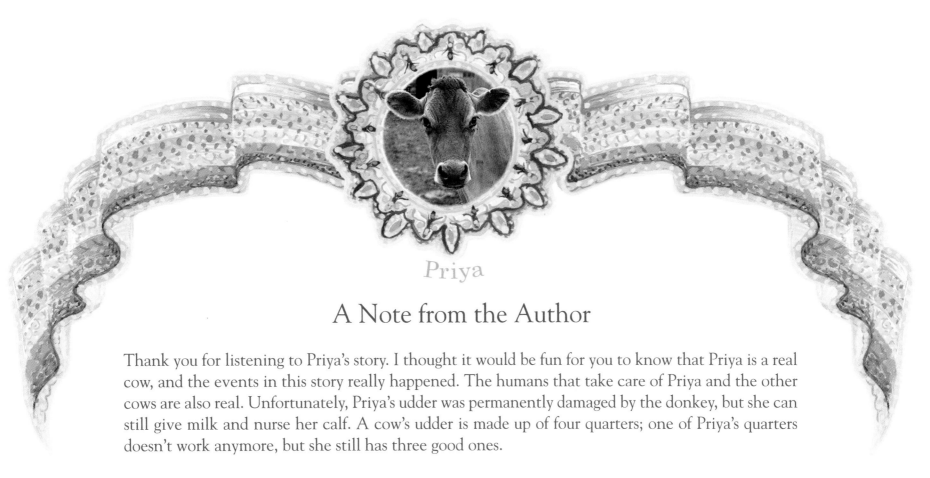

Priya

A Note from the Author

Thank you for listening to Priya's story. I thought it would be fun for you to know that Priya is a real cow, and the events in this story really happened. The humans that take care of Priya and the other cows are also real. Unfortunately, Priya's udder was permanently damaged by the donkey, but she can still give milk and nurse her calf. A cow's udder is made up of four quarters; one of Priya's quarters doesn't work anymore, but she still has three good ones.

When Katherine told me how Priya placed her head on her feet (after Katherine had refused to send her back to her previous owner), it made me understand how intelligent and emotional cows are. They really can sense what is happening in their environment and how it will affect them. All cows have their favorite cow friends, and their family bonds are very strong.

Priya and other cows that Katherine has come to know over the years inspired the creation of The Cows Foundation. She wanted to find a way to provide support for as many cows as possible. Throughout the ages, cows have given nourishing and delicious dairy products to all of humanity. They deserve a long and happy life.

For more information go to www.thecowsfoundation.org or email priyasownstory@gmail.com

About the Author and the Artist

Originally from Australia and a family of generations of dairy farmers, the author Carole Davey is a former Montessori School teacher and a longtime member of the Mother Divine Program. Debby Henning, the illustrator, is also an alumna of the Mother Divine Program and Cooper Union for the Advancement of Art and Science.

The Mother Divine Program comprises groups of women around the world dedicated to realizing their full spiritual potential—enlightenment—and enlivening world peace through the nourishing power of bliss and coherence. Through their extended collective practice of the Transcendental Meditation® and TM-Sidhi® programs, they silently and yet most efficiently nourish our world family in an unseen (but verifiable) manner from the deepest level of Nature's functioning—the simplest state of human awareness, the silent field of pure consciousness.

Why was this story written? A small herd of "Ahimsa" cows came to live on a property where a group of Mother Divine are residing. They experience first-hand the loving, compassionate care that Ahimsa farming brings. Ahimsa means nonviolent. These cows are allowed to live out their natural lifespan and have the joy of nursing and caring for their young calves. The milk received from these truly happy cows is like nectar, the sweetest ambrosia.

Proceeds from this book will go towards caring for as many cows as possible and helping to create a better world.